Edition Schott

o-Bibliothek

Camille Saint-Saëns
1835 – 1921

Allegro appassionato

for Violoncello and Piano
für Violoncello und Klavier
pour Violoncelle et Piano

B minor / h-Moll / Si mineur
opus 43

Edited by / Herausgegeben von / Edité par
Maria Kliegel

CB 186
ISMN 979-0-001-14074-4

www.schott-music.com

SCHOTT

Mainz · London · Berlin · Madrid · New York · Paris · Prague · Tokyo · Toronto
© 2007 SCHOTT MUSIC GmbH & Co. KG, Mainz · Printed in Germany

Vorwort

Niemand kennt die Musik der ganzen Welt besser als Monsieur Saint-Saëns, lobte Claude Debussy seinen Komponistenkollegen. Und nur wenige, darf man hinzufügen, haben ein derartig umfangreiches und alle Gattungen abdeckendes Gesamtwerk hinterlassen wie er: Symphonische und dramatische Musik, Vokal- und Kammermusik, Klavier-, Militär- und Ballettmusik hat Camille Saint-Saëns (1835 – 1921) komponiert, aber auch mit *L'Assassinat du Duc de Guise* 1908 die erste originale Filmmusik geliefert.

Mit seinem *Konzert Nr. 1 a-Moll*, op. 33, komponierte der französische Musiker einen „Klassiker" der Violoncelloliteratur: Wenn es auch nach der Uraufführung eher befremdet aufgenommen wurde – zu neu war die durchkomponierte Form, die Einbindung von Solopart in den Orchestersatz –, hat es sich heute einen Stammplatz im Konzertsaal erobert. Doch Saint-Saëns hat das Violoncello noch mit weiteren Solowerken bedacht, mit einem zweiten Konzert, mit zwei Sonaten und einer Suite mit Klavierbegleitung sowie mit dem Solosatz aus seinem wohl bekanntesten Werk, dem *Carneval der Tiere*: dem *Schwan*. Skepsis, ja oft Ablehnung der zeitgenössischen Kritik insbesondere in seiner Heimat ziehen sich jedoch über viele Jahre wie ein roter Faden durch die Biographie von Saint-Saëns: *Zweifellos hat der Komponist ein ausgeprägtes Stilempfinden, das jedoch stets überschattet wird von veralteten Ideen und einem offensichtlichen Schwanken zwischen den Formen von gestern, denen von heute und oft sogar denen von morgen*, schrieb ein Zeitgenosse in der *Revue et Gazette Musicale* über das erste *Klaviertrio F-Dur* op. 18. Erst in den letzten Lebensjahren konnte Camille Saint-Saëns auch in Frankreich die gebührende Anerkennung finden, die er bislang bereits im Ausland erfahren hatte. Heute steht seine Bedeutung für die Entwicklung der französischen Musik im 19. Jahrhundert außer Frage.

Das *Allegro appassionato h-Moll* op. 43 entstand 1875, in einer Zeit, in der sich Saint-Saëns zunehmend den Anfeindungen des Pariser Publikums und der Presse ausgesetzt sah. Er komponierte, nach heimlich vollzogener Eheschließung, unermüdlich, doch war ihm damit kein großer Erfolg beschieden. Das brillante wie melodisch eingängige Werk für Violoncello und Klavier in Rondoform wurde später vom Komponisten selbst orchestriert und eignet sich insbesondere als effektvolles Zugabestück. Zu Edition: In der Klavierstimme sind die Originalphrasierungsbögen des Violoncelloparts abgedruckt. Wer sich über die originale Phrasierung des Komponisten informieren will, sei auf die Klavierstimme verwiesen.

Wolfgang Birtel

Preface

'Nobody knows more about music all over the world than Monsieur Saint-Saëns', said Claude Debussy in praise of his fellow composer. There can be few, one might add, who have left behind such an extensive body of work, representing every musical genre: Camille Saint-Saëns (1835 – 1921) composed symphonic and dramatic music, vocal and chamber music, piano, military and ballet music – and, with *L'Assassinat du Duc de Guise* in 1908, the first original film music.

With his *Concerto No. 1 in A minor* Op. 33 this French musician composed one of the classics of the cello repertoire. Those who listened to the first performance were rather disconcerted by the through-composed form and found the integration of the solo part into the orchestral writing too innovative, but today this concerto has won a place as a regular feature in the concert hall. Saint-Saëns did write other solo works for the cello: a second concerto, two sonatas and a suite with piano accompaniment, as well as the solo movement from what is probably his best known work, the *Carnival of the Animals: the Swan*. Yet a sceptical and often dismissive response from contemporary critics, especially in his native land, was a recurring theme in Saint-Saëns' life over many years: 'There can be no doubt that this composer has a definite sense of style – yet this is constantly overshadowed by outmoded ideas and an evident vacillation between the forms of yesteryear, those of today and even those of tomorrow', wrote a contemporary reviewing his *Piano Trio in F major* Op. 18 in the *Revue et Gazette musicale*. Not until the last years of his life did Camille Saint-Saëns receive the recognition he deserved in France, having enjoyed far greater success abroad up to that point. Nowadays his significance in the development of French music in the 19th Century is unquestioned.

The *Allegro appassionato in B minor* Op. 43 was written in 1875, at a time when Saint-Saëns was increasingly confronted with animosity from Parisian audiences and the press. After getting married in secret he carried on composing tirelessly, but his work was not welcomed with much success. The composer himself later orchestrated this brilliant and melodically accessible work for cello and piano in rondo form; it makes a particularly impressive encore piece. Editor's note: The piano part contains the original phrasing slurs of the violoncello part. Anyone who wants to learn more about the original phrasing of the composer should have a look at the piano part.

Wolfgang Birtel
Translation Julia Rushworth

Préface

« *Saint-Saëns est l'homme qui sait le mieux la musique du monde entier* ». C'est par ces mots que Claude Debussy faisait l'éloge de son homologue. Et, faudrait-il ajouter, bien peu de compositeurs ont laissé un œuvre aussi nombreux, couvrant tous les genres : Camille Saint-Saëns (1835 – 1921) a composé des musiques symphoniques et dramatiques, vocales et de chambre, pour piano, militaires, de ballet – mais aussi, avec *L'Assassinat du Duc de Guise* en 1908, la première musique de film originale.

Son *Concerto n° 1 en la mineur*, op. 33, est un « classique » de la littérature pour violoncelle : accueilli plutôt avec un étonnement irrité lors de la première – la forme, composée de bout en bout, l'intégration du solo dans la partie de l'orchestre, étaient par trop nouvelles, il a aujourd'hui une place attitrée dans les salles de concert. Pourtant, Saint-Saëns a consacré au violoncelle d'autres œuvres solistes, un second concerto, deux sonates et une suite à accompagnement de piano, ainsi que le mouvement soliste de la plus célèbre de ses œuvres, le *Cygne* du *Carnaval des animaux*. Le scepticisme, allant même jusqu'au rejet, de la critique de son temps, en particulier dans son pays natal, traverse cependant comme un fil rouge, pendant de longues années, la biographie de Saint-Saëns : « *[Ce] compositeur, il a un incontestable mérite de style, obscuri à chaque instant par des idées vieillottes, par une hési-tation évidente entre les formes d'autrefois, celles d'aujourdh'hui et même, souvent, celles de demain* », écrivait un contemporain dans la *Revue et Gazette Musicale* au sujet de son premier *Trio pour piano, violon et violoncelle en fa majeur* op. 18. Ce n'est que dans les dernières années de sa vie que Camille Saint-Saëns fut enfin reconnu et apprécié également en France comme il le mérite et comme il l'était déjà à l'étranger. Aujourd'hui, son importance pour l'évolution de la musique française au XIXème est incontestée.

L'*Allegro appassionato en si mineur* op. 43 vit le jour en 1875, époque à laquelle Saint-Saëns était de plus en plus exposé aux attaques du public parisien et de la presse. Après s'être marié en secret, il composait inlassablement, mais sans grand succès. Cette œuvre pour violoncelle et piano, dans la forme du *rondo*, brillante et à la mélodie rapidement familière, fut plus tard mise en orchestre par le compositeur lui-même, et est particulièrement bien adaptée pour un rappel impressionnant. Note de l'editeur: La partie piano contient les liaisons de phrasé originales de la partie violoncelle. Pour ceux qui veulent savoir plus sur le phrasé original du compositeur, voyez la partie piano.

Wolfgang Birtel
Traduction Martine Paulauskas

Allegro appassionato
opus 43

Camille Saint-Saëns
1835–1921

© 2007 Schott Music GmbH & Co. KG, Mainz

52 008

Das widerrechtliche Kopieren von Noten ist gesetzlich verboten und kann privat- und strafrechtlich verfolgt werden.
Unauthorised copying of music is forbidden by law, and may result in criminal or civil action.

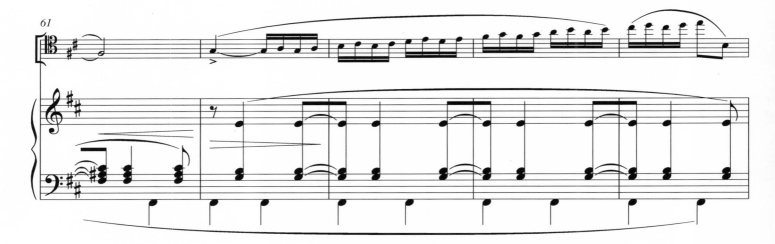

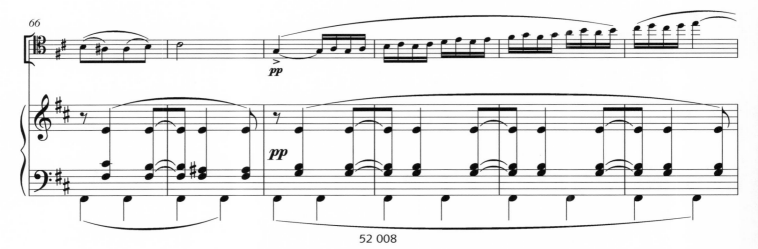

*) 8va ad libitum (Vorschlag der Herausgeberin / Editor's suggestion)

Schott Music, Mainz 52 008

Violoncello

Allegro appassionato
opus 43

Camille Saint-Saëns
1835–1921

*) 8va ad libitum (Vorschlag der Herausgeberin / Editor's suggestion)

© 2007 Schott Music GmbH & Co. KG, Mainz   52 008

Das widerrechtliche Kopieren von Noten ist gesetzlich verboten und kann privat- und strafrechtlich verfolgt werden.
Unauthorised copying of music is forbidden by law, and may result in criminal or civil action.

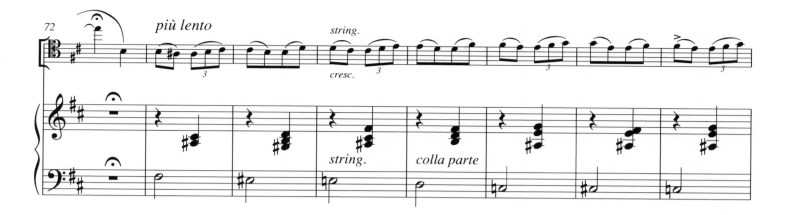

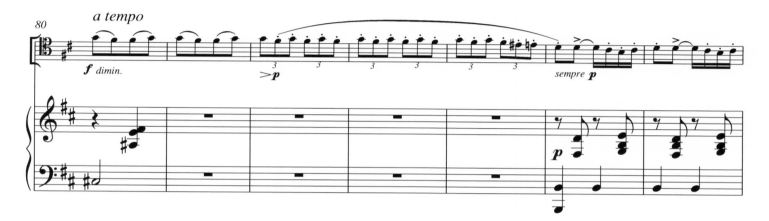

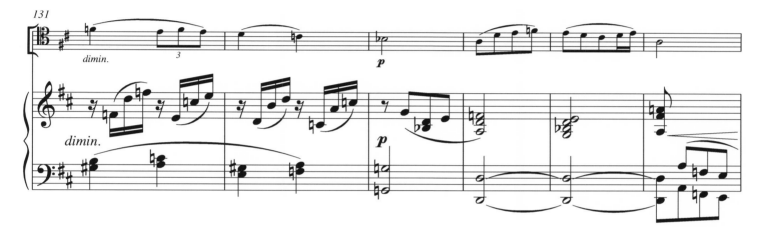

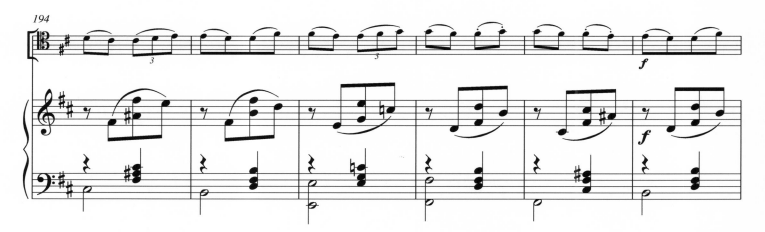

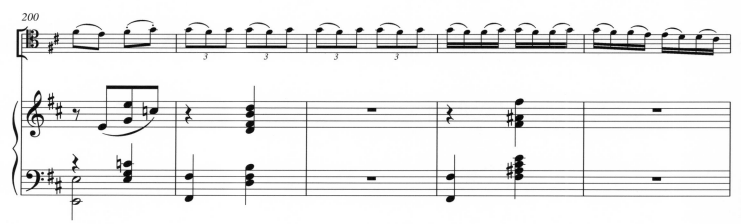

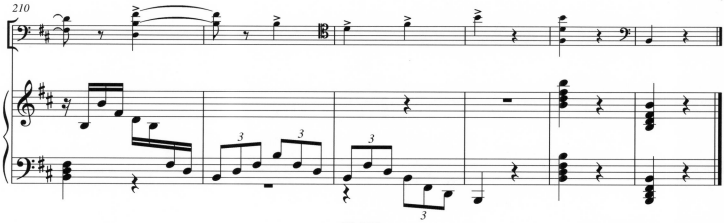

Schott Music, Mainz 52 008